SONGWORDS 1978-1989

the Cure

Fiction   Omnibus Press

ISBN 0.7119.1951.8

Order No. OP45574

Exclusive distributors:

Book Sales Limited,
8/9 Frith Street,
London W1V 5TZ, UK.

Music Sales Corporation,
225 Park Avenue South,
New York, NY 10003, USA.

Music Sales Pty Limited,
120 Rothschild Avenue,
Rosebery, NSW 2018, Australia.

To the Music Trade only:
Music Sales Limited,
8/9 Frith Street,
London W1V 5TZ, UK.

Printed in Scotland

A catalogue record for this title
is available from The British Library.

A BOOK OF SONGWORDS

THE CURE

1978 - 1989

TYPED BY SUE HOPKINS

EDITED BY ROBERT SMITH

PUT TOGETHER BY TONY FOO

COVER ART BY MAYA

A FICTION BOOK

CONTENTS

A BOOK OF SONG WORDS

1978 - 1980

Robert Smith,

Laurence Tolhurst,

Michael Dempsey.

KILLING AN ARAB

Standing on the beach
With a gun in my hand
Staring at the sea
Staring at the sand
Staring down the barrel
At the arab on the ground
See his open mouth
But hear no sound

I'm alive
I'm dead
I'm the stranger
Killing an arab

I can turn
And walk away
Or I can fire the gun
Staring at the sky
Staring at the sun
Whichever I choose
It amounts to the same

Absolutely nothing

I'm alive
I'm dead
I'm the stranger
Killing an arab

Feel the steel butt jump
Smooth in my hand
Staring at the sea
Staring at the sand
Staring at myself
Reflected
In the eyes of the dead man on the beach

The dead man
On the beach

I'm alive
I'm dead
I'm the stranger
Killing an arab

10:15 SATURDAY NIGHT

10:15
Saturday night
And the tap drips
Under the striplight
And I'm sitting
In the kitchen sink
And the tap drips
Drip drip drip drip drip drip...

Waiting
For the telephone to ring
And I'm wondering
Where she's been
And I'm crying
For yesterday
And the tap drips
Drip drip drip drip drip drip...

It's always the same...

ACCURACY

We sit in the same room
Side by side
I give you the wrong lines
Feed you

Look into my eyes
We both smile
I could kill you
Without trying

That's accuracy
Practice all day for accuracy

Mirror mirror
On the wall...

GRINDING HALT

No light
No people
No speak
No people
No cars
No people
No food
No people

Stopped
Short
Grinding halt
Everything's coming to a grinding halt

No sound
No people
No clocks
No people
No fine
No people
No me
No people

Stopped
Short
Grinding halt
Everything's coming to a grinding halt

Slow down
Slow down
No people
Slow down

ANOTHER DAY

The sun rises slowly
On another day
The Eastern sky grows cold
Winter in water colours
Shades of grey

Something
Something holds me hypnotized...

I stare at the window
Stare at the window
Waiting for the day to go
Winter in water colours
Shades of grey

OBJECT

You know you turn me on
Eyes so wide and legs so long
But don't try to talk to me
I won't listen to your lies
You're just an object in my eyes

Sophisticated smile
You seduce in such fine style
But don't try to fool me
Cos I can see through your disguise
You're just an object in my eyes

But I don't mind
I just don't care
I've got no objections
To you touching me...

You know just what to do
Lick your lips
And I want you
But don't try to hold me
Cos I don't want any ties
You're just an object in my eyes

But I don't mind
I just don't care
I've got no objections
To you touching me...

You're just an object
Object object object
You're just an object

SUBWAY SONG

Midnight in the subway
She's on her way home
She tries hard not to run
But she feels she's not alone
Echoes of footsteps
Follow close behind
But she dare not turn around...

Turn around

MEATHOOK

I went into the butchers
I said I wanted wanted wanted some
Meat
Pass me some of that steak over there
It looks so
Sweet

I lost my heart to a meathook

That butcher man was some lady
He really stole my heart
He hung me up on his meathook
A real piece of
Slaughterhouse art

I lost my heart to a meathook

There's a meathook in my heart
Tearing me all apart
Ripping out my insides
But I just can't get away
I can't leave my
Meathook

FIRE IN CAIRO

Slowly fading blue
The Eastern hollows catch
The dying sun
Night time follows
Silent and black
Mirror pool mirrors
The lonely place
Where I meet you

See your head
In the fading light
And through the dark
Your eyes shine bright

And burn like fire
Burn like fire in Cairo
Burn like fire
Burn like fire in Cairo

Shifting crimson veil
Silken hips slide
Under my hand
Swollen lips whisper my name
And I yearn
You take me in your arms
And start to burn

F.I.R.E.I.N.C.A.I.R.O
Then the heat disappears
And the mirage
Fades away

F.I.R.E.I.N.C.A.I.R.O

Burn like a fire in Cairo
Burn like a fire
Blaze like a fire in Cairo
Blaze like a fire
Flare
With a wonderful light
Like a fire in Cairo
Burn like fire
Burn like fire in Cairo

SO WHAT?

Cake icing and decorating set
Special offer
Only £3.30
Save £1.52 on recommended retail price
Give your cakes and pies a professional look
With this superb decorating set

I'm not meant to be here
But so what?
Nobody's taken your place
Nobody's taken your place

Each set includes
A turntable
A nine inch icing bag
With six high definition nozzles and adaptor
And a fifteen inch food decorating bag
With three piping nozzles
Please send off this leaflet
Post it today

And if you knew
Nothing could replace you
If you were sane
Your heart wouldn't ache
But so what?
So what?
So what?

Order now
Allow twenty-one days
For delivery
The offer closes
31st December 1979

British Sugar Bureau
When I told you what I...
And I...

And I wouldn't ask you to pretend
That we were one
And still another time...
Forget all the lies
Forgive me the wounds
And all the world was used to love
And yes we'd still be happy in another time...
But so what?

So please send me icing and decorating sets
I enclose a cheque and
Postal Order number...

So what?
So what?

IT'S NOT YOU

You wear your smile
Like it was going out of fashion
Dress to inflame
But douse any ideas of passion
You carry your love in a trinket
Hanging round your throat
Always inviting
Always exciting
But I must not take off my coat

Well I'm tired of hanging around
I want someone new
I'm not sure who I've got in mind
But I know
It's not you

You ask me questions
That I never wanted to hear
I am the only one
Just until you finish this year
I would murder you
If I had an alibi
Here in my hand
But you just laugh
Cos you don't understand

That I'm tired of hanging around
I want somebody new
I'm not sure
Who I've got in mind
But I know that it's not you
It's not you
It's not you
It's not you

THREE IMAGINARY BOYS

Walk across the garden
In the footsteps of my shadow
See the lights out
No-one's home
In amongst the statues
Stare at nothing in
The garden moves
Can you help me?

Close my eyes
And hold so tightly
Scared of what the morning brings
Waiting for tomorrow
Never comes
Deep inside
The empty feeling
All the night time leaves me
Three imaginary boys

Slipping through the door
Hear my heart beat
In the hallway
Echoes
Round and round
Inside my head
Drifting up the stairs
I see the steps behind me
Disappearing
Can you help me?

Close my eyes
And hold so tightly
Scared of what the morning brings
Waiting for tomorrow
Never comes
Deep inside
The empty feeling
All the night time leaves me
Three imaginary boys sing in my
Sleep sweet child
The moon will change your mind

See the cracked reflection
Standing still
Before the bedroom mirror
Over my shoulder
But no-one's there
Whispers in the silence
Pressing close behind me
Pressing close behind
Can you help me?

Can you help me?

BOYS DON'T CRY

I would say I'm sorry
If I thought that it would change your mind
But I know that this time
I have said too much
Been too unkind

I try to laugh about it
Cover it all up with lies
I try and
Laugh about it
Hiding the tears in my eyes
Cos boys don't cry

I would break down at your feet
And beg forgiveness
Plead with you
But I know that
It's too late
And now there's nothing I can do

So I try to laugh about it
Cover it all up with lies
I try to
Laugh about it
Hiding the tears in my eyes
Cos boys don't cry

I would tell you
That I loved you
If I thought that you would stay
But I know that it's no use
That you've already
Gone away

Misjudged your limit
Pushed you too far
Took you for granted
I thought that you needed me more

Now I would do most anything
To get you back by my side
But I just
Keep on laughing
Hiding the tears in my eyes
Cos boys don't cry
Boys don't cry

PLASTIC PASSION

Plastic passion is a hard to handle
Plastic passion is a sold out scandal
Oh it's a plastic passion

Plastic passion is the ladies lover
Pastic passion is the marble mother
Oh it's a plastic passion

Plastic passion is a diamond delight
Plastic passion is the nadir of night
Oh it's a plastic passion

Plastic passion is a hyoscine heart
Plastic passion is a transparent tart
Oh it's a plastic passion

Plastic passion is a gold guarantee
This plastic passion is murdering me
Oh it's a plastic passion

JUMPING SOMEONE ELSES TRAIN

Don't say what you mean
You might spoil your face
If you walk in the crowd
You won't leave any trace
It's always the same
You're jumping someone elses train

It won't take you long
To learn the new smile
You have to adapt
Or you'll be out of style
It's always the same
You're jumping someone elses train

If you pick up on it quick
You can say you were there
Again and again and again
You're jumping on someone elses train

It's the latest wave
That you've been craving for
The old ideal
Was getting such a bore
Now you're back in line
Going not quite as far
But in half the time
Everybody's happy
They're finally all the same
Cos everyone's jumping
Everybody elses train

Jumping someone elses train
Jumping someone elses train

I'M COLD

You're begging me to stay
But I'm laughing in your face
You're so desperate
Not to let those years of care
All go to waste
But it was you who wanted love
Not romance
You have to pay the price
My body may be made of fire
But my soul is made of ice

I'm me
I'm cold
I'm cold
I'm told
I'd love to love you girl
But my body
Has just been sold

WORLD WAR

Dressed in Berlin black
I was only playing
Disguise my words to fool you
From what I was saying
Mud trench
Meat stench
The fatherland is looking on
Grip you in a luger lock
This will be the big one

World war
No-one would believe me
World war
No-one's a winner
No-one's a loser
Just a dead friend

Heaven heaven
Give me pride
Give me a golden hand
Smash them with an iron rule
Spit them out like sand
Sit and wait
Then run like hell
Run like hell one time again
Sow the seeds of hate
Underneath destruction

DO THE HANSA

Ein zwei drei vier
Steve oh yeah
Platinum all the way
Do the hansa
Do the hansa
Etc etc

PILLBOX TALES

Electric line
Racing time
Fire down the wall
Spinning around
The killing ground
It makes you look so small
Henna years
The stinging tears
Flesh on the railway track
The screaming queen
On the TV screen
Is never coming back

Don't suffer no more
Just step inside and listen
Listen to my pillbox tales

Your special days
Your winning ways
You're living out the past
You're lying lies
And tying ties
And running much too fast
But you feel so sick
If you run too quick
And wishing every day
Wishing you were all alone
Wishing you were years away

Don't suffer no more
Just step inside and listen
Listen to my pillbox tales

HEROIN FACE

Spit out the shout of a warning
Death is an honour with doubts
So you live in the end
And you mistrust the start
Because you don't think it counts

But you'll pay for yourself
You'll pay for yourself
You're just a heroin face

You see a heroin face in the mirror
And someone is clutching your breath
And you believe in the needle of night
You're only doing your best

But you'll pay for yourself
You'll pay for yourself

You believe in the needle of night
And someone is clutching your breath
So you mistrust the start
By always running away
But you'll never come back

You're just a heroin face
Heroin face

1980 - 1981

Robert Smith,

Laurence Tolhurst,

Simon Gallup,

Matthieu Hartley.

PLAY FOR TODAY

It's not a case of doing what's right
It's just the way I feel that matters
Tell me I'm wrong
I don't really care

It's not a case of share and share alike
I take what I require
I don't understand...
You say it's not fair

You expect me to act
Like a lover
Consider my moves
And deserve the reward
To hold you in my arms
And wait...
For something to happen

It's not a case of telling the truth
Some lines just fit the situation
You call me a liar
You would anyway

It's not a case of aiming to please
You know you're always crying
It's just your part
In the play for today

SECRETS

Secrets
Share with another girl
Talking all night in a room
All night
Everything slowing down
I wish I was yours...

Strangers
Nobody knows we love
I catch your eyes in the dark
One look relives the memory
Remember me
The way I used to be

IN YOUR HOUSE

I play at night in your house
I live another life
Pretending to swim
In your house
I change the time in your house
The hours I take
Go so slow...

I hear no sound in your house
Silence
In the empty rooms
I drown at night in your house
Pretending to swim...

THREE

Scream

A FOREST

Come closer and see
See into the trees
Find the girl
While you can
Come closer and see
See into the dark
Just follow your eyes
Just follow your eyes

I hear her voice
Calling my name
The sound is deep
In the dark
I hear her voice
And start to run
Into the trees
Into the trees

Suddenly I stop
But I know it's too late
I'm lost in a forest
All alone
The girl was never there
It's always the same
I'm running towards nothing
Again and again and again

M

Hello image
Sing me a line from your favourite song
Twist and turn
But you're trapped in the light
All the directions were wrong

You'll fall in love with somebody else
Tonight

Help yourself
But tell me the words
Before you fade away
You reveal all the secrets
To remember the end
And escape someday

You'll fall in love with somebody else
Again tonight

Take a step
You move in time
But it's always back...
The reasons are clear
Your face is drawn
And ready for the next attack

AT NIGHT

Sunk deep in the night
I sink in the night
Standing alone underneath the sky
I feel the chill of ice
On my face
I watch the hours go by
The hours go by

You sleep
Sleep in a safe bed
Curled and protected
Protected from sight
Under a safe roof
Deep in your house
Unaware of the changes at night

At night
I hear the darkness breathe
I sense the quiet despair
Listen to the silence
At night
Some-one has to be there
Some-one has to be there

SEVENTEEN SECONDS

Time slips away
And the light begins to fade
And everything is quiet now
Feeling is gone
And the picture disappears
And everything is cold now
The dream had to end
The wish never came true
And the girl
Starts to sing

Seventeen seconds
A measure of life
Seventeen seconds

1981 - 1982

Robert Smith,

Laurence Tolhurst,

Simon Gallup.

THE HOLY HOUR

I kneel and wait in silence
As one by one the people slip away
Into the night
The quiet and empty bodies
Kiss the ground before they pray
Kiss the ground
And slip away...

I sit and listen dreamlessly
A promise of salvation makes me stay
Then look at your face
And feel my heart pushed in
As all around the children play
The games they tired of yesterday
They play

I stand and hear my voice
Cry out
A wordless scream at ancient power
It breaks against stone
I softly leave you crying
I cannot hold what you devour
The sacrifice of pennance
In the holy hour

PRIMARY

The innocence of sleeping children
Dressed in white
And slowly dreaming
Stops all time
I slow my steps and start to blur
So many years have filled my heart
I never thought I'd say those words

The further we go
And older we grow
The more we know
The less we show

The very first time I saw your face
I thought of a song
And quickly changed the tune
The very first time I touched your skin
I thought of a story
And rushed to reach the end
Too soon

Oh remember
Please
Don't change

And so the fall came
Thirteen years
A shining ring
And how I could forget your name
The air no longer in my throat
Another perfect lie is choked
But it always feels the same

So they close together
Dressed in red and yellow
Innocent forever
Sleeping children in their blue soft rooms
Still dream

OTHER VOICES

Whisper your name in an empty room
You brush past my skin
As soft as fur
Taking hold
I taste your scent
Distant noises
Other voices
Pounding in my broken head
Commit the sin
Commit yourself
And all the other voices said
Change your mind
You're always wrong

Come around at Christmas
I really have to see you
Smile at me slyly
Another festive compromise
But I live with desertion
And eight million people
Distant noises
Other voices
Pulsing in my swinging arms
Caress the sound
So many dead
And all the other voices said
Change your mind
You're always wrong

ALL CATS ARE GREY

I never thought that I would find myself
In bed amongst the stone
The columns are all men
Begging to crush me
No shapes sail on the dark deep lakes
And no flags wave me home

In the caves
All cats are grey
In the caves
The textures coat my skin
In the death cell
A single note
Rings on and on and on...

THE FUNERAL PARTY

Two pale figures
Ache in silence
Timeless
In the quiet ground
Side by side
In age and sadness

I watched
And acted wordlessly
As piece by piece
You performed your story
Moving through an unknown past
Dancing at the funeral party

Memories of childrens dreams
Lie lifeless
Fading
Lifeless
Hand in hand with fear and shadows
Crying at the funeral party

I heard a song
And turned away
As piece by piece
You performed your story
Noiselessly across the floor
Dancing at the funeral party

DOUBT

Stop my flight to fight
And die
And take stand to change my life
So savage with red desperation
I clench my hands
You draw your claws
A hidden rage consumes my heart
As fuelled by years of wasted time
I close my eyes
And tense myself
And screaming
Throw myself in fury over the edge
And into your blood

Tear at flesh
And rip at skin
And smash at doubt
I have to break you
Fury drives my vicious blows
I see you fall but still I strike you
Again and again
Your body falls
The movement is sharp and clear and pure
And gone
I stop and kneel beside you
Drained of everything but pain

Screaming throw myself in fury
Over the edge and into your blood

Kiss you once and see you writhe
Hold you close and hear you cry
Kiss your eyes and finish your life
Finish your life

Again and again
Your body falls
The movement is sharp and clear and pure
And gone
I stop and kneel beside you
Knowing I'll murder you again tonight

THE DROWNING MAN

She stands twelve feet above the flood
She stares
Alone
Across the water

The loneliness grows and slowly
Fills her frozen body
Sliding downwards

One by one her senses die
The memories fade
And leave her eyes
Still seeing worlds that never were
And one by one the bright birds leave her...

Starting at the violent sound
She tries to turn
But final
Noiseless
Slips and strikes her soft dark head
The water bows
Receives her
And drowns her at it's ease

I would have left the world all bleeding
Could I only help you love
The fleeting shapes
So many years ago
So young and beautiful and brave

Everything was true
It couldn't be a story

I wish it all was true
I wish it couldn't be a story
The words all left me
Lifeless
Hoping
Breathing like the drowning man

Oh Fuschia
You leave me
Breathing like the drowning man
Breathing like the drowning man

FAITH

Catch me if I fall
I'm losing hold
I can't just carry on this way
And every time
I turn away
Lose another blind game
The idea of perfection holds me...
Suddenly I see you change
Everything at once
The same
But the mountain never moves

Rape me like a child
Christened in blood
Painted like an unknown saint
There's nothing left but hope
You voice is dead
And old
And always empty
Trust in me through closing years
Perfect moments wait
If only we could stay...
Please
Say the right words
Or cry like the stone white clown
And stand
Lost forever in a happy crowd

No one lifts their hands
No one lifts their eyes
Justified with empty words
The party just gets better and better

I went away alone
With nothing left
But faith

CHARLOTTE SOMETIMES

All the faces
All the voices blur
Change to one face
Change to one voice
Prepare yourself for bed
The light seems bright
And glares on white walls
All the sounds of
Charlotte sometimes
Into the night with
Charlotte sometimes

Night after night she lay alone in bed
Her eyes so open to the dark
The streets all looked so strange
They seemed so far away
But Charlotte did not cry
The people seemed so close
Playing expressionless games
The people seemed
So close
So many
Other names

Sometimes I'm dreaming
Where all the other people dance
Sometimes I'm dreaming
Charlotte sometimes
Sometimes I'm dreaming
Expressionless the trance
Sometimes I'm dreaming
So many different names
Sometimes I'm dreaming
The sounds all stay the same
Sometimes I'm dreaming
She hopes to open shadowed eyes
On a different world
Come to me
Scared princess
Charlotte sometimes...

On that bleak track
(See the sun is gone again)
The tears were pouring down her face
She was crying and crying for a girl
Who died so many years before...

Sometimes I dream
Where all the other people dance
Sometimes I dream
Charlotte sometimes
Sometimes I dream
The sounds all stay the same
Sometimes I'm dreaming
There are so many different names
Sometimes I dream
Sometimes I dream...

Charlotte sometimes crying for herself
Charlotte sometimes dreams a wall around herself
But it's always with love
With so much love it looks like
Everything else
Of Charlotte sometimes
So far away
Glass sealed and pretty
Charlotte sometimes

SPLINTERED IN HER HEAD

Shape is still
Asleep
With the toys
As tall as men
The pictures in the hallway
Turning inside
Whispers
Unseen
Jumping against the sky
Slipping away
He looks
For the last time...

ONE HUNDRED YEARS

It doesn't matter if we all die
Ambition in the back of a black car
In a high building there is so much to do
Going home time
A story on the radio...

Something small falls out of your mouth
And we laugh
A prayer for something better
A prayer
For something better

Please love me
Meet my mother
But the fear takes hold
Creeping up the stairs in the dark
Waiting for the death blow

Stroking your hair as the patriots are shot
Fighting for freedom on the television
Sharing the world with slaughtered pigs
Have we got everything?
She struggles to get away...

The pain
And the creeping feeling
A little black haired girl
Waiting for saturday
The death of her father pushing her
Pushing her white face into the mirror
Aching inside me
And turn me around
Just like the old days
Just like the old days

Caressing an old man
And painting a lifeless face
Just a piece of new meat in a clean room
The soldiers close in under a yellow moon
All shadows and deliverance
Under a black flag
A hundred years of blood
Crimson
The ribbon tightens round my throat
I open my mouth
And my head bursts open
A sound like a tiger thrashing in the water
Thrashing in the water
Over and over
We die one after the other
Over and over
We die one after the other after the other...

It feels like a hundred years
One hundred years...

A SHORT TERM EFFECT

Movement
No movement
Just a falling bird
Cold as it hits the bleeding ground
He lived and died
Catch sight
Cover me with earth
Draped in black
Static
White sound

A day without substance
A change of thought
An atmosphere that rots with time
Colours that flicker in water
A short term effect

Scream
As she tries to push him over
Helpless and sick
With teeth of madness
Jump jump dance and sing
Sideways across the desert
A charcoal face
Bites my hand
Time is sweet
Derange and disengage everything

A day without substance
A change of thought
The atmosphere rots with time
Colours that flicker in water
A short term effect

An echo
And a strangers hand
A short term effect
An echo
And a strangers hand
A short term effect

THE HANGING GARDEN

Creature kissing in the rain
Shapeless in the dark again
In the hanging garden
Please don't speak
In the hanging garden
No one sleeps

Catching haloes on the moon
Gives my hands the shapes of angels
In the heat of the night
The animals scream
In the heat of the night
Walking into a dream...

Fall fall fall fall
Into the walls
Jump jump out of time
Fall fall fall fall
Out of the sky
Cover my face as the animals cry

Creatures kissing in the rain
Shapeless in the dark again
In a hanging garden
Change the past
In a hanging garden
Wearing furs
And masks

Fall fall fall fall
Into the walls
Jump jump out of time
Fall fall fall fall
Out of the sky
Cover my face as the animals die
In the hanging garden

SIAMESE TWINS

I chose an eternity of this
Like falling angels
The world disappeared
Laughing into the fire
Is it always like this?
Flesh and blood and the first kiss
The first colours
The first kiss

We writhed under a red light
Voodoo smile
Siamese twins
A girl at the window looks at me for an hour
Then everything falls apart
Broken inside me
It falls apart

The walls and the ceiling move in time
Push a blade into my hands
Slowly up the stairs
And into the room
Is it always like this?

Dancing in my pocket
Worms eat my skin
She glows and grows
With arms outstreched
Her legs around me...

In the morning I cried

Leave me to die
You won't remember my voice
I walked away and grew old
You never talk
We never smile
I scream
You're nothing
I don't need you anymore
You're nothing

It fades and spins...

Sing out loud
We all die
Laughing into the fire

Is it always like this?

THE FIGUREHEAD

Sharp and open
Leave me alone
And sleeping less every night
As the days become heavier and weighted
Waiting
In the cold light
A noise
A scream tears my clothes as the figurines tighten
With spiders inside them
And dust on the lips of a vision of hell
I laughed in the mirror for the first time in a year

A hundred other words blind me with your purity
Like an old painted doll in the throes of dance
I think about tomorrow
Please let me sleep
As I slip down the window
Freshly squashed fly
You mean nothing
You mean nothing

I can lose myself in chinese art and american girls
All the time
Lose me in the dark
Please do it right
Run into the night
I will lose myself tomorrow
Crimson pain
My heart explodes
My memory in a fire
And someone will listen
At least for a short while

I can never say no to anyone but you

Too many secrets
Too many lies
Writhing with hatred
Too many secrets
Please make it good tonight
But the same image haunts me
In sequence
In despair of time

I will never be clean again
I touched her eyes
Pressed my stained face
I will never be clean again

Touch her eyes
Press my stained face
I will never be clean again

A STRANGE DAY

Give me your eyes
That I might see the blind man kissing my hands
The sun is humming
My head turns to dust as he plays on his knees

And the sand
And the sea grows
I close my eyes
Move slowly through drowning waves
Going away on a strange day

And I laugh as I drift in the wind
Blind
Dancing on a beach of stone
Cherish the faces as they wait for the end
A sudden hush across the water
And we're here again

And the sand
And the sea grows
I close my eyes
Move slowly through drowning waves
Going away
On a strange day

My head falls back
And the walls crash down
And the sky
And the impossible
Explode
Held for a moment I remember a song
An impression of sound
Then everything is gone
Forever

A strange day

COLD

Scarred
Your back was turned
Curled like an embryo
Take another face
You will be kissed again
I was cold as I mouthed the words
And crawled across the mirror
I wait
Await the next breath
Your name
Like ice into my heart

A shallow grave
A monument to the ruined age
Ice in my eyes
And eyes like ice don't move
Screaming at the moon
Another past time
Your name
Like ice into my heart

Everything as cold as life
Can no one save you?
Everything
As cold as silence
And you will never say a word

Your name
Like ice into my heart

PORNOGRAPHY

A hand in my mouth
A life spills into the flowers
We all look so perfect
As we all fall down
In an electric glare
The old man cracks with age
She found his last picture
In the ashes of the fire
An image of the queen
Echoes round the sweating bed
Sour yellow sounds inside my head
In books
And films
And in life
And in heaven
The sound of slaughter
As your body turns

But it's too late

One more day like today and I'll kill you
A desire for flesh
And real blood
And I'll watch you drown in the shower
Pushing my life through your open eyes

I must fight this sickness
Find a cure...

1982 - 1983

Robert Smith,

Laurence Tolhurst.

LET'S GO TO BED

Let me take your hand
I'm shaking like milk
Turning
Turning blue
All over the windows and the floors
Fires outside in the sky
Look as perfect as cats
The two of us
Together again
But it's just the same
A stupid game

But I don't care if you don't
And I don't feel if you don't
And I don't want it if you don't
And I won't say it
If you don't say it first

You think you're tired now
But wait until three
Laughing at the Christmas lights
You remember from December
All of this then back again
Another girl
Another name
Stay alive but stay the same
It's just the same
A stupid game

But I don't care if you don't
And I don't feel if you don't
And I don't want it if you don't
And I won't play it
If you don't play it first

You can't even see now
So you ask me the way
You wonder if it's real
Because it couldn't be rain
Through the right doorway
And into the white room
It used to be the dust that would lay here
When I came here alone

Doo doo doo doo
Doo doo doo doo
Let's go to bed

JUST ONE KISS

Remember the time that you rained all night
The queen of Siam in my arms
Remember the time that the islands sank
But nobody opened their eyes

Remember that time that the trees fell down
The wood crashing through the wall
Remember the sound that could wake the dead
But nobody woke up at all

Somebody died for this
Somebody died for just one kiss

Remember the time that the sky went black
We waited alone on the sands
Remember the taste of the raging sea
But nobody held out their hands

Somebody died for this
Somebody died
For just one kiss

Just one kiss
Just one kiss

THE WALK

I called you after midnight
Then ran until I burst
I passed the howling woman
And stood outside your door

We walked around a lake
And woke up in the rain
And everyone turned over
Troubled in their dreams again

Visiting time is over
And so we walk away
And both play dead then cry out loud
Why we always cry this way?

I kissed you in the water
And made your dry lips sing
I saw you look
Like a Japanese baby
In an instant I remembered everything

I called you after midnight
Then ran until my heart burst
I passed the howling woman
And stook outside your door

I kissed you in the water
And made your dry lips sing
I saw you look
Like a Japanese baby
In an instant I remembered everything

THE UPSTAIRS ROOM

I love it all
These games we play
I close my eyes
You run away
I'm sure I asked you to stay
But now you're gone
And so I feel the grey
Pulse in my head
I turn off the lights and crawl into bed
I try to think of sunshine
But my body goes wet
With the first crash of thunder

I don't think I can know
Anyone but you dear
That's for sure

When it gets to four
It's my turn to go
Oh the kiss
So alcoholic and slow
Arranging me for Saturday
I thought you would know
That I always sleep
Alone

I don't think I can love
Anyone but you
Dear
That's for sure

The upstairs room is cool and bright
We could go up there in summer
And dance all night

Your sister started talking at a minute after ten
So everyone jumped up
And then fell over again
In April you can join them
And stare at me
At the ghost from your past...

SPEAK MY LANGUAGE

It was only yesterday
Waving arms across the street
Your white face left me blue
How can I say all the things
I have to say to you
Oh all the people here
All look the same
The little time I spend with you
We drink each other dry

Mammnnarghaassstmmetc!
Speak my language!

It was only yesterday
My eyes touched yours across the street
We cut the words
And waved goodbye
And dropped off the edge of the world

Mammnnarghaassstmmetc!
Speak my language!

MR PINK EYES

You look so cool
Oh I don't think
Just fall over
Be like me
Mr Pink Eyes

Your mind is blank
And mine's away
Oh you can't see
You can't smell
Mr Pink Eyes

It's got to be jazz
That's what she wants
You are so vile
Mr Pink Eyes

Oh give me a look
Give me a look
Or sit on my head
Or jump on my foot
Do something!

PIGGY IN THE MIRROR

Shapes in the drink like Christ
Cracks in the pale blue wall
I'm walking slowly and quickly but always away
Twisting twisting to the floor

Flowers in your mouth and the same dry song
The routine from laughter land
16 white legs and a row of teeth
They watch you in secrecy

You're dying for the hope is gone
From here we go nowhere again
I'm trapped in my face and I'm changing too much
I can't climb out the way I fell in

Jump with me
For that old forgotten dance
The midnight sun will burn you up
Your life is cold
Your life is hard
Your life is too much for words

These occasions are such a relief
Another point
Another view to send
We start to talk
And it's all so safe...
I feed you in my dreams

Footsteps on a wire
High above my head
The stain reveals my real intention
I'm the waiting beast
I'm the twisted nerve
As I dance dance
Back to the body in my bed

Look at the piggy
Piggy in the mirror

BIRDMAD GIRL

This girl has got a smile
That can make me cry
This girl just burns with love
She's burning burning deep outside

Night time night time
Sets my house on fire
I'll turn into the melting man
I'll lose my life
To feel I feel desire

Oh I should feel
Like a polar bear...
It's impossible

She flies outside this cage
Singing girlmad words
I keep her dark thoughts deep inside
As black as stone
And mad as birds

Wild wild wild
And never turn away
Sends me all her love
She sends me everything
She sends me everywhere

Oh I could be
A polar bear...
It's impossible

I try to talk
The sky goes red
I forget
So fill in my head
With some of this
Some of that
Some of every words she says

Oh I should be
A polar bear...
But it's impossible

THE CATERPILLAR

Flicka flicka flicka
Here you are
Cata cata cata
Caterpillar girl
Flowing in
And filling up my hopeless heart
Oh never never go

Dust my lemon lies
With powder pink and sweet
The day I stop
Is the day you change
And fly away from me

You flicker
And you're beautiful
You glow inside my head
You hold me hypnotized
I'm mesmerised
Your flames
The flames that kiss me dead

NEW DAY

New day
In heaven the ground is waiting
For the dust
The seed
My love once more
I shout
New day

Hold the air and gasp in life
This solid dance
This cold cold night
Is gone...
The dark heat throbs
The fools sweat swims
The hazy lights
The deadly sins
Are gone...

Crack the stone
Invade my head
Dropping honey dropping dead again
The silence shouts
Across the gap
Another dreaming
Love me again
Shout...

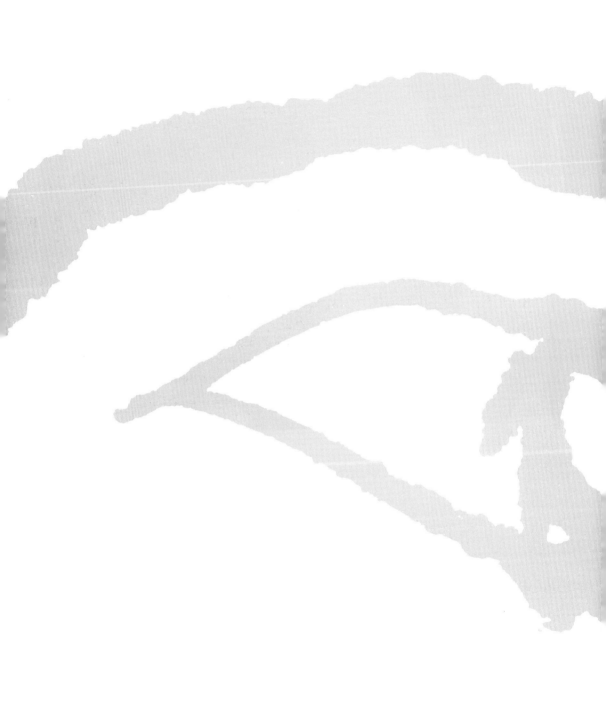

1982 - 1983

Robert Smith.

THE DREAM

You're too far away
Too far away to touch
And this mother's love inside me
Hurts too much
Prettily waving
Playing on the sands
Dreaming of everything
Dancing
Dancing in our hands
Dancing
Dancing

Dizzy dizzy dizzy
As I speak
Like a tumbling cat
I watch in fascination
Like a vampire bat
Don't do it don't do it
Don't do it don't do it
Don't give it away
We'll use it up tomorrow
If we don't use it today

Rest your head
Oh just put it outside
All wrapped up in ribbons
The night
The dream
The time love died

We pushed it in our mouths
Pushed it deep inside
All wrapped up in ribbons
The night
The dream
The time love died
The night
The dream
The time
Love died

LA MENT

Today there was a tragedy
Underneath the bridge
A man walked
Cold and blue
Into La Ment
The sky coloured perfect
As the man slipped away
Waving with a last vanilla smile

Somewhere at a table
Two drowned fools
Smoking
Drinking water as they talked
Of how they loved our lady
And oh the smell as candles die

One more ice cream river body
Flowed underneath the bridge
Underneath the bridge

THE LOVECATS

We move like cagey tigers
We couldn't get closer than this
The way we walk
The way we talk
The way we stalk
The way we kiss
We slip through the streets
While everyone sleeps
Getting bigger and sleeker
And wider and brighter
We bite and scratch and scream all night
Let's go
And throw
All the songs we know...

Into the sea
You and me
All these years and no one heard
I'll show you in spring
It's a treacherous thing
We missed you hissed the lovecats

We're so wonderfully wonderfully wonderfully
Wonderfully pretty
Oh you know that I'd do anything for you
We should have each other to tea huh?
We should have each other with cream
Then curl up in the fire
And sleep for a while
It's the grooviest thing
It's the perfect dream

Into the sea
You and me
All these years and no one heard
I'll show you in spring
It's a treacherous thing
We missed you hissed the lovecats

We're so wonderfully wonderfully wonderfully
Wonderfully pretty
Oh you know that I'd do anything for you
We should have each other to dinner huh?
We should have each other with cream
Then curl up in the fire
Get up for a while
It's the grooviest thing
It's the perfect dream

Hand in hand
Is the only way to land
And always the right way round
Not broken in pieces
Like hated little meeces
How could we miss
Someone as dumb as this

I love you ... let's go
Oh ... solid gone...
How could we miss
Someone as dumb as this?

SHAKE DOG SHAKE

Ha ha ha
Wake up in the dark
The aftertaste of anger in the back of my mouth
Spit it on the wall
And cough some more
And scrape my skin with razor blades

And make up in the new blood
And try to look so good
Follow me
Make up in the new blood
And follow me to where the real fun is
Ha ha ha

As stale and selfish as a sick dog
Spurning sex like an animal of god
I'll tear your red hair by the roots
And hold you blazing
Hold you cherished in the dead electric light

Your face
I'll never see you this way again
I captured it so perfectly
As if I knew you'd disappear away

Shake dog shake

You hit me again
You howl and hit me again
The same sharp pain
Wakes me in the dark
And cuts me from my throat to my pounding heart
My heart
My shaking heart

Shake dog shake

But we slept all night in the virgins bed
And dreamed of death
And breathed like sick dogs
We slept all night in the virgins bed
And breathed like death
And dreamed of sick dogs

Shake dog shake

Wake up in the new blood
Make up in the new blood
Shake up in this new blood
And follow me to where the real fun is

Shake dog shake dog shake

WAILING WALL

The holy city breathed
Like a dying man
It moved with hopeful tears
With the tears of the blind

And on and on as the night drew in
Through broken streets
That sucked me in
My feet were bare and cut with stones
With walking to the promised land

I pushed through crowds
Through seas of prayer
Through twisting hands and choking air
A vulture at the wailing wall
I circled
Waiting

GIVE ME IT

Get away from me
Get your fingers out of my face
This room's so hot
This room's so hot

I break the walls

Get away from me
Leave me alone
Like the pig on the stairs
Hanging
In a groovy purple shirt

Gasping for air
I'm gasping for air
I'm gasping for love
I'm gasping for air

Slit the cats like cheese
Then eat the sweet sticky things
Suck harder suck harder
Suck your insides inside out

Blood thick swimming round your feet
As you're choking
Choking
Choking on the fleshy words

Give me it give me it give me it
Deaden my glassy mind
Give me it give me it
Make me blind
One step back and one step down
And slip the needles in my side

My head is cold
My hands are cold
My heart is cold
My heart is black
And stops every fucking night
Every night
I wait until it stops

Sing birds sing birds sing birds sing
Get away

DRESSING UP

Going under slowly
It never seems too late
Going under so slow

Dressing up to kiss
Dressing up to touch all this

I'm dressing up to dance all week
I'm dressing up to sleep

Dressing up to kiss
Dressing up to be all this

I could eat your face
I could eat all of you
Oh this night will never let me go...

Going under slowly
Never seems too late
Going under slowly
You'll pick me up again

THE EMPTY WORLD

As stiff as toys
And tall as men
And swaying like the wind torn trees
She talked about the empty world
With eyes like poisoned birds

She talked about the armies
That marched inside her head
And how they made her dreams go bad
But oh how happy she was!
How proud she was!
To be fighting in the war
In the empty world

BANANAFISHBONES

Curl into a ball like you have more fun
That would make it faster
Why do you do it do you do it do you act like you
Why do you do it do you act like you?

Don't fight
Go red and blue and black and white
Sell this sell this
Or leave it senseless like a suck on a gun?
Put a piece of metal in your head you said
Make you dead
Make you hippa hippa hippa hippa

A palace of stones
Of your bananafishbones
I'd buy you a hundred years old
To celebrate our difference
Theorise and talk yourself
Until you're tired and old

Disappear everywhere and watch me
Pull my lips apart
Exploit inspire encourage
Be responsible for this
Ha ha!

I don't think
I don't think
I make use of all this time
Oh kill me kiss me once
And then we'll throw it away
And then we'll throw it away

Turn off the lights
And tell me about the games you play

THE TOP

I don't care
If only I could say that
And not feel so sick and scared
I don't care
If only I could say that
If only my eyes would close

It's Jesus brilliant
You used to laugh
Walking these gorgeous blocks
This top is the place
Where nobody goes
You just imagine
You just imagine it all

Everyday I lie here
And know that it's true
All I really want is you
Please come back
Please come back
Like all the other ones do

Please come back
All of you...

THROW YOUR FOOT

It's funny how your face gets bigger
Gets bigger in this atmosphere
And your mouth goes dry
With every move you try
It's so funny here

Jumping around
Click click click
When you're so slow
It's like the world is stopping

Fifteen times I try this
And every time I faint
You look at me and
Start to tell the joke
About the man who couldn't stop
Hiccupping...

It would be so perfect
If you would just fall out the window

Throw you foot away
You're tired and your face is grey
Like the sad old fool
You groove

Hey hey hey

HAPPY THE MAN

I'll never understand
(Come closer and I'll whisper)
Who was that standing in the rain?
If only I could remember
What he said
(And how it all began)

Happy the man
With the face that smiles

But it has to have a name
(Something strong, something faithful, something pure)
How does he look so safe?

He'll never
Never turn away
Happy the man

1985

Robert Smith.

THE EXPLODING BOY

I couldn't hear a word you said
I couldn't hear at all
You talked until your tongue fell out
And then you talked some more
I knew if I turned
I'd turn away from you
And I couldn't look back

Tell yourself we'll start again
Tell yourself its not the end
Tell yourself it couldn't happen
Not this way
Not today

A FEW HOURS AFTER THIS...

The look before I go
Is the look for you
You only have to look and it will all come true
And we can fall outside
Into the fizzy night
Or pull me down in here
You know its all the same
I only want to see if you are happy again
Or we can roll around
And find out upside down

A few hours after this and we're apart again
Like two white checks
Like opposite poles
In a secret game
(Like nothing like these I suppose...)
I really should have known by the cut of your smile
That the answer would be simple
It still took you a while to get it out of me
I thought you'd do it easily

Just put your hands around my heart
And squeeze me until I'm dry
I never thought you'd ever start to ever ask me why

I never saw you again...

INBETWEEN DAYS

Yesterday I got so old
I felt like I could die
Yesterday I got so old
It made me want to cry
Go on go on
Just walk away
Go on go on
Your choice is made
Go on go on
And disappear
Go on go on
Away from here

And I know I was wrong
When I said it was true
That it couldn't be me and be her
Inbetween without you
Without you

Yesterday I got so scared
I shivered like a child
Yesterday away from you
It froze me deep inside
Come back come back
Don't walk away
Come back come back
Come back today
Come back come back
Why can't you see
Come back come back
Come back to me

And I know I was wrong
When I said it was true
That it couldn't be me and be her
Inbetween without you
Without you

KYOTO SONG

A nightmare of you
Of death in the pool
Wakes me up at quarter to three
I'm lying on the floor of the night before
With a stranger lying next to me
A nightmare of you
Of death in the pool
I see no further now than this dream
The trembling hands of the trembling man
Hold my mouth
To hold in a scream

I try to think
To make it slow
If only here is where I go
If this is real
I have to see
I turn on fire
And next to me
It looks good
It tastes like nothing on earth
It looks good
It tastes like nothing on earth
Its so smooth it even feels like skin
It tells me how it feels to be new

It tells me how it feels to be new
A thousand voices whisper it true
It tells me how it feels to be new
And every voice belongs
Every voice belongs to you

THE BLOOD

Tell me who doesn't love
What can never come back
You can never forget how it used to feel
The illusion is deep
Its as deep as the night
I can tell by your tears you remember it all

I am paralyzed by the blood of Christ
Though it clouds my eyes
I can never stop

How it feels to be dry
Walking bare in the sun
Every mirage I see is a mirage of you
As I cool in the twilight
Taste the salt on my skin
I recall all the tears
All the broken words

I am paralyzed by the blood of Christ
Though it clouds my eyes
I can never stop

When the sunsets glow drifts away from you
You'll no longer know
If any of this was really true at all

SIX DIFFERENT WAYS

This is stranger than I thought
Six different ways inside my heart
And every one I'll keep tonight
Six different ways go deep inside

I'll tell them anything at all
I know I'll give them more and more

I'll tell them anything at all
I know I'll give the world and more
They think I'm on my hands and head
This time they're much too slow

Six sides to every lie I say
Its that American voice again
"It was never quite like this before
Not one of you is the same"

This is stranger than I ever thought
Six different ways inside my heart
And every one I'll keep tonight
Six different ways go deep inside

PUSH

Go go go
Push him away
No no no
Don't let him stay

He gets inside to stare at her
The seeping mouth
The mouth that knows
The secret you
Always you
A smile to hide the fear away
Oh smear this man across the walls
Like strawberries and cream
Its the only way to be

Exactly the same clean room
Exactly the same clean bed
But I've stayed away too long this time
And I've got too big to fit this time...

THE BABY SCREAMS

Heaven
Give me a sign
Waiting for the sun to shine
Pleasure fills up my dreams
And I love it
Like a baby screams

Its so useless
How can you be proud
When you're sinking into the ground
Into the ground fills up my dreams
And I love it
Like a baby screams

Couldn't ask for more you said
Take it all
And strike me
Strike me dead

Waiting again
Waiting
Like I waited before
Waiting again
Waiting here for nothing at all
Heaven fills up my dreams
And I love it
Like a baby screams

Couldn't ask for more you said
Couldn't ever let it end
Take it all
Take it all
And strike me dead

Heaven!
Heaven!

CLOSE TO ME

I've waited hours for this
I've made myself so sick
I wish I'd stayed asleep today
I never thought this day would end
I never thought tonight could ever be
This close to me

Just try to see in the dark
Just try to make it work
To feel the fear before you're here
I make the shapes come much too close
I pull my eyes out
Hold my breath
And wait until I shake

But if I had your faith
Then I could make it safe and clean
If only I was sure
That my head on the door was a dream...

I've waited hours for this
I've made myself so sick
I wish I'd stayed asleep today
I never thought this day would end
I never thought tonight could ever be
This close to me

But if I had your face
I could make it safe and clean
If only I was sure
That my head on the door
Was a dream...

A NIGHT LIKE THIS

Say goodbye on a night like this
If its the last thing we ever do
You never looked as lost as this
Sometimes it doesn't even look like you
It goes dark
It goes darker still
Please stay...
But I watch you like I'm made of stone
As you walk away

I'm coming to find you if it takes me all night
A witch hunt for another girl
For always and ever is always for you
Your trust
The most gorgeously stupid thing I ever cut in the world

Say hello on a day like today
Say it every time you move
The way that you look at me now
Makes me wish I was you
It goes deep
It goes deeper still
This touch
And the smile and the shake of your head...

I'm coming to find you if it takes me all night
Can't stand here like this anymore
For always and ever is always for you
I want it to be perfect
Like before...
I want to change it all

I want to change

SCREW

When you screw up your eyes
When you screw up your face
When you throw out your arms
And keep changing your shape
Taste the taste in your mouth
Taste the taste on your tongue
On the film on your eyes of the way I've become

What do I do when you screw up your eyes?
What do I do when you screw up your face?
What do I do
When you throw out your arms
Fall on the floor
And keep changing your shape?
Jump right into your mouth?
Jump around on your tongue?

And the film on your eyes of the way I've become
Makes me sick at the way that I try
Anything in the world
To impress that I'm doing this
Only for you

SINKING

I am slowing down
As the years go by
I am sinking
So I trick myself
Like everybody else

The secrets I hide
Twist me inside
They make me weaker
So I trick myself
Like everybody else

I crouch in fear and wait
I'll never feel again
If only I could remember
Anything at all

A MAN INSIDE MY MOUTH

I woke up at seven and my body was vibrating
I was wrapped up in a blanket
I was grey
Damp and sore
The bedroom was an engine and my heartbeat was erratic
(Like I think I'm at the racing
Like the night before)
I remember one girl standing
One was sitting on the ground
One was holding me up
The other pulling me down
And I couldn't decide which one was real
Because there wasn't a sound
(Like I was pregnant again...)

"Don't move don't blink don't even breathe" she said
"Or the photograph will spoil
And cut you off at the head"
So I was sucking
I was sucking like a fat lady would
But I couldn't hold it down another second
(Bleagh!)
"Don't twitch don't shout don't think don't even breathe" she said
"Or the photograph will spoil and cut you off at the head"
So I was sweating
I was sweating like a fat lady would
And I woke up
With a man inside my mouth
(This won't hurt at all...)

STOP DEAD

Let me forget
Let me forget
Or let me go let me go
I'll keep it quiet as a whisper
I'll keep it low low low
Never
The biggest word I ever heard
Stop dead
Stop dead
You're getting too close

Before you ever opened your eyes
I moved about a million ways
I killed about a million people
And filled about half a day
Before you even opened your eyes
You had to have to ask me who
I love it...
I mean you

My face was in your hands
You looked into my eyes
You said I tasted right
And swallowed me alive

1987

Robert Smith.

THE KISS

Kiss me kiss me kiss me
Your tongue is like poison
So swollen it fills up my mouth

Love me love me love me
You nail me to the floor
And push my guts all inside out

Get it out get it out get it out
Get your fucking voice
Out of my head

I never wanted this
I never wanted any of this
I wish you were dead
I wish you were dead

I never wanted any of this
I wish you were dead
Dead
Dead
Dead

CATCH

Yes I know who you remind me of
A girl I think I used to know
Yes I'd see her when the days got colder
On those days when it felt like snow

You know I even think that she stared like you
She used to just stand there and stare
And roll her eyes right up to heaven
And make like I just wasn't there

And she used to fall down a lot
That girl was always falling
Again and again
And I used to sometimes try to catch her
But never even caught her name

And sometimes we would spend the night
Just rolling about on a floor
And I remember
Even though it felt soft at the time
I always used to wake up sore...

You know I even think that she smiled like you
She used to just stand there and smile
And her eyes would go all sort of far away
And stay like that for quite a while

And I remember she used to fall down a lot
That girl was always falling
Again and again
And I used to sometimes try to catch her
But never even caught her name

Yes I sometimes even tried to catch her
But never even caught her name

TORTURE

I'm in the room without a light
The room without a view
I'm here for one more treacherous night
Another night with you
It tortures me to move my hands
To try to move at all
And pulled
My skin so tight it screams
And screams and screams
And pulls some more

Hanging like this
Like a vampire bat
Hanging like this
Hanging on your back
I'm helpless again

My body is cut and broken
It's shattered and sore
My body is cut wide open
I can't stand anymore
It tortures me to move my hands
To try to move at all
And pulled
My skin so tight it screams
And screams and screams
And screams for more

Hanging like this
Like a vampire bat
Hanging like this hanging on your back
Oh it's torture
And I'm almost there
It's torture
But I'm almost there

It's torture
But I'm almost there
It's torture
But I'm almost there

IF ONLY TONIGHT WE COULD SLEEP

If only tonight we could sleep
In a bed made of flowers
If only tonight we could fall
In a deathless spell

If only tonight we could slide
Into deep black water
And breathe
And breathe...

Then an angel would come
With burning eyes like stars
And bury us deep
In his velvet arms

And the rain would cry
As our faces slipped away
And the rain would cry

Don't let it end...

WHY CAN'T I BE YOU?

You're so gorgeous I'll do anything
I'll kiss you from your feet
To where your head begins
You're so perfect you're so right as rain
You make me
Make me hungry again

Everything you do is irresistable
Everything you do is simply kissable
Why can't I be you?

I'll run around in circles
Til I run out of breath
I'll eat you all up
Or I'll just hug you to death
You're so wonderful
Too good to be true
You make me
Make me hungry for you

Everything you do is simply delicate
Everything you do is quite angelicate
Why can't I be you?

You turn my head when you turn around
You turn the whole world upside down
I'm smitten I'm bitten I'm hooked I'm cooked
I'm stuck like glue
You make me
Make me hungry for you

Everything you do is simply dreamy
Everything you do is quite delicious
Why can't I be you?
Why can't I be you?
Why can't I be you?

You're simply elegant!!!

THE SNAKEPIT

Well we're a mile under the ground
And I'm thinking that it's Christmas
And I'm kissing you hard
Like I've got very important business
And no-one knows
And no-one sees us
Because they're drinking their selves senseless
And I'm writhing
And I'm writhing
And I'm writhing in the snakepit

Well I'm out in a car
And it's just full of stupid girls
And I've forgotten how to speak
And I just can't remember a word
And my eyes feel like they're bursting
And they're splitting like plums
And I'm writhing
And I'm writhing
And I'm writhing in the snakepit

HOW BEAUTIFUL YOU ARE....

You want to know why I hate you?
Well I'll try and explain...
You remember that day in Paris
When we wandered through the rain
And promised to each other
That we'd always think the same
And dreamed that dream
To be two souls as one

And stopped just as the sun set
And waited for the night
Outside a glittering building
Of glittering glass and burning light...

And in the road before us
Stood a weary greyish man
Who held a child upon his back
A small boy by the hand
The three of them were dressed in rags
And thinner than air
And all six eyes stared fixedly on you

The father's eyes said "Beautiful!
How beautiful you are!"
The boy's eyes said
"How beautiful!
She shimmers like a star!"
The child's eyes uttered nothing
But a mute and utter joy
And filled my heart with shame for us
At the way we are

I turned to look at you
To read my thoughts upon your face
And gazed so deep into your eyes
So beautiful and strange
Until you spoke
And showed me understanding is a dream
"I hate these people staring
Make them go away from me!

The father's eyes said "Beautiful!
How beautiful you are!"
The boy's eyes said
"How beautiful!
She glitters like a star!"
The child's eyes uttered nothing
But quiet and utter joy
And stilled my heart with sadness
For the way we are

And this is why I hate you
And how I understand
That no-one ever knows or loves another

Or loves another

HEY YOU!!!

Hey you!!!
Yes you
Yes you the one that looks like Christmas
Come over here and kiss me
Kiss me

Hey you!!!
Yes you
Yes you the one that looks delirious
Come over here and kiss me
Kiss me

JUST LIKE HEAVEN

"Show me how you do that trick
The one that makes me scream" she said
"The one that makes me laugh" she said
And threw her arms around my neck
"Show me how you do it
And I promise you I promise that
I'll run away with you
I'll run away with you"

Spinning on that dizzy edge
I kissed her face and kissed her head
And dreamed of all the different ways I had
To make her glow
"Why are you so far away?" she said
"Why won't you ever know that I'm in love with you
That I'm in love with you"

You
Soft and only
You
Lost and lonely
You
Strange as angels
Dancing in the deepest oceans
Twisting in the water
You're just like a dream

Daylight licked me into shape
I must have been asleep for days
And moving lips to breathe her name
I opened up my eyes
And found myself alone alone
Alone above a raging sea
That stole the only girl I loved
And drowned her deep inside of me

You
Soft and only
You
Lost and lonely
You
Just like heaven

ALL I WANT

Tonight I'm feeling like an animal
Tonight I'm howling inside
Tonight I'm feeling like an animal
Tonight I'm going wild

And all I want is to be with you again
And all I want is to hold you like a dog
And all I want is to be with you again
With you again
Just to hold you like a dog

Tonight I'm screaming like an animal
Tonight I'm losing control
Tonight I'm screaming like an animal
Tonight oh I'm getting so low

And all I want is to be with you again
And all I want is to hold you like a dog
And all I want is to be with you again
With you again
Just to hold you like a dog
That's all I want

HOT HOT HOT!!!

The first time I saw lightning strike
I saw it underground
Six deep feet below the street
The sky came crashing down
For a second that place was lost in space
Then everything went black
I left that basement burning
And I never went back

The second time I saw it strike
I saw it at sea
It lit up all the fish like rain
And rained them down on me
For a second that boat was still afloat
Then everything went black
I left it underwater
And I never went back

Hey hey hey!!!
But I like it when that lightning comes
Hey hey hey!!!
Yes I like it a lot
Hey hey hey!!!
Yes I'm jumping like a jumping jack
Dancing screaming itching squealing fevered
Feeling hot hot hot!!!

The third time I saw lightning strike
It hit me in bed
It threw me around
And left me for dead
For a second that room was on the moon
Then everything went black
I left that house on fire
And I never went back

Hey hey hey!!!
But I like it when that lightning comes
Hey hey hey!!!
Yes I like it a lot
Hey hey hey!!!
Yes I'm jumping like a jumping jack
Dancing screaming itching squealing fevered
Feeling hot hot hot!!!

ONE MORE TIME

I'd love to touch the sky tonight
I'd love to touch the sky
So take me in your arms
And lift me like a child
And hold me up so high
And never let me go
Take me
Take me in your arms tonight

Hold me
Hold me up so high
And never let me down
Hold me
Hold me up so high
To touch the sky
Just one more time

Take me in your arms tonight
Take me in your arms
Just one more time
Just one more time
Just one more time

LIKE COCKATOOS

She walked out of her house
And looked around
At all the gardens that looked
Back at her house
(Like all the faces
That quiz when you smile...)

And he was standing
At the corner
Where the road turned dark
A part of shiny wet
Like blood the rain fell
Black down on the street

And kissed his feet she fell
Her head an inch away from heaven
And her face pressed tight
And all around the night sang out
Like cockatoos

"There are a thousand things" he said
"I'll never say those things to you again"
And turning on his heel
He left a trace of bubbles
Bleeding in his stead

And in her head
A picture of a boy who left her
Lonely in the rain
(And all around the night sang out
Like cockatoos)

ICING SUGAR

You're delicious
Dreaming
Slack jawed
Green eyed
Rub my nose in
Icing sugar
Smooth as
When this cold and deadly
Blade
Kisses the fruit
So soft
And gently breathing
Under your skin

Oh I'll empty you
I'll empty you
As empty as a boy can be
As empty
As a boy can be

THE PERFECT GIRL

You're such a strange girl
I think you come from another world
You're such a strange girl
I really don't understand a word
You're such a strange girl
I'd like to shake you around and around
You're such a strange girl
I'd like
To turn you
All upside down

You're such a
Strange girl
The way you look like you do
You're such a strange girl
I want
To be with you

I think I'm falling
I think I'm falling in
I think I'm falling in love with you
With you

A THOUSAND HOURS

For how much longer can I howl into this wind?
For how much longer
Can I cry like this?

A thousand wasted hours a day
Just to feel my heart for a second
A thousand hours just thrown away
Just to feel my heart for a second

For how much longer can I howl into this wind?

SHIVER AND SHAKE

You're just a waste of time
You're just a babbling face
You're just three sick holes that run like sores
You're a fucking waste
You're like a slug on the floor
Oh you're useless and ugly
And useless and ugly
And I shiver and shake
When I think of how you make me hate

I want to smash you to pieces
I want to smash you up and screaming
I want to smash you helpless
Down on the floor
Smash you until you're not here anymore

And I shiver and shake
Shiver and shake

FIGHT

Sometimes there's nothing to feel
Sometimes there's nothing to hold
Sometimes there's no time to run away
Sometimes you just feel so old
The times it hurts when you cry
The times it hurts just to breathe
And then it seems like there's no-one left
And all you want is to sleep

Fight fight fight
Just push it away
Fight fight fight
Just push it until it breaks
Fight fight fight
Don't cry at the pain
Fight fight fight
Or watch yourself burn again
Fight fight fight
Don't howl like a dog
Fight fight
Just fill up the sky
Fight fight fight
Fight til you drop
Fight fight fight
And never never
Never stop

Fight fight fight
Fight fight fight

So when the hurting starts
And when the nightmares begin
Remember you can fill up the sky
You don't have to give in
You don't have to give in

Never give in
Never give in
Never give in

A JAPANESE DREAM

I'm going back to the land of the blind
Back to the land where the sun never shines
I'm going back there and I'm hoping to find
Everything just as it was before
I left it all behind

I slept at nights there hysterically
Twisted and turned
But I just couldn't get free
Opened my eyes
But I still couldn't see
But I could feel her
China white girl

So I get down on the floor
Like I am worshipping god
Burning like a monkey
I get down on the floor
Like I am praying to the lord
Burning like a monkey

Mmmmmm that was a japanese dream alright
The sound of the storm
And the flickering light
And the way that her scent used to fill up the night like.
Like her scent used to fill up the night

So I get down on the floor
Like I am worshipping god
Burning like a monkey
I get down on the floor
Like I am praying to the lord
Burning like a monkey

Just look at me now
Just look at me this way
It looks like I am quite insane
It looks like I am trying to eat off my face
It looks like I'm going to the land of the blind anyway
Back where the sun never shines
Back to the land of the blind
Back in a japanese dream

BREATHE

Breathe
Breathe on me
Be like you used to be
Breathe on me

Move in me
Be like you used to be
Move in me
Move in me

Be with me
Be like you used to be
With me
With me

CHAIN OF FLOWERS

Please wake up
It's so dark and cold
Please wake up
I feel so alone
And I feel so scared
That you're going away
And I feel so scared...

All I want is summer
Stories from before
Just like the day you tried to hide
Behind the churchyard wall
And fell asleep before I came
I found you
In a chain of flowers
Sleeping like a marble girl
Sleeping in another world...

I'll never tell you
Of all the different ways
You make me so afraid...

SNOW IN SUMMER

High up on this mountain
The whole world looks so small
And all the rivers
Run away
Slipping in your deep green heart
I drink you as I swim
And I'm sliding
And I'm sliding with you
Slide beneath my skin

Sleek and deep
And salty sweet
You open up in me
Just like the snow in summer

High up on this mountain
The whole world looks so small
And all the rivers
Run away
Slipping in your soft white heart
I drink you as I swim
And I'm falling
And I'm falling with you
Fall beneath my skin

Sleek and deep
And salty sweet
You come
And close in me
Just like the snow in summer

Just like the snow in summer
As it melts
Into the sea

SUGAR GIRL

Oh I wish I could find it funny
You laughing like that
But instead I change into a rage
And run around
Without a face
I wish I could find it funny
When you never come back
But I don't suppose I'll ever know
The how to keep you
Goodbye sugar girl

Goodbye sugar girl

1989

Robert Smith.

PLAINSONG

"I think it's dark
And it looks like rain"
You said
"And the wind is blowing
Like it's the end of the world"
You said
"And it's so cold
It's like the cold if you were dead"
And then you smiled
For a second

"I think I'm old
And I'm feeling pain"
You said
"And it's all running out
Like it's the end of the world"
You said
"And it's so cold
It's like the cold if you were dead"
And then you smiled
For a second

Sometimes you make me feel
Like I'm living at the edge of the world
Like I'm living at the edge of the world
"It's just the way I smile"
You said

THE SAME DEEP WATER AS YOU

Kiss me goodbye
Pushing out before I sleep
Can't you see I try
Swimming the same deep water as you is hard
"The shallow drowned
Lose less than we"
You breathe
The strangest twist upon your lips
"And we shall be together..."

"Kiss me goodbye
Bow your head and join with me"
And face pushed deep
Reflections meet
The strangest twist upon your lips
And disappear
The ripples clear
And laughing
Break against your feet
And laughing
Break the mirror sweet
"So we shall be together..."

"Kiss me goodbye"
Pushing out before I sleep
It's lower now
And slower now
The strangest twist upon your lips
But I don't see
And I don't feel
But tightly hold up silently
My hands before my fading eyes
And in my eyes
Your smile
The very last thing before I go...

I will kiss you I will kiss you
I will kiss you forever on nights like this
I will kiss you I will kiss you
And we shall be together...

CLOSEDOWN

I'm running out of time
I'm out of step
And closing down
And never sleep for wanting hours
The empty hours of greed
And uselessly
Always the need
To feel again the real belief
Of something more than mockery
If only I could fill
My heart with love

LOVESONG

Whenever I'm alone with you
You make me feel like I am home again
Whenever I'm alone with you
You make me feel like I am whole again

Whenever I'm alone with you
You make me feel like I am young again
Whenever I'm alone with you
You make me feel like I am fun again

However far away
I will always love you
However long I stay
I will always love you
Whatever words I say
I will always love you
I will always love you

Whenever I'm alone with you
You make me feel like I am free again
Whenever I'm alone with you
You make me feel like I am clean again

However far away
I will always love you
However long I stay
I will always love you
Whatever words I say
I will always love you
I will always love you

LULLABY

On candystripe legs the spiderman comes
Softly through the shadow of the evening sun
Stealing past the windows of the blissfully dead
Looking for the victim shivering in bed
Searching out fear in the gathering gloom
And suddenly!
A movement in the corner of the room!
And there is nothing I can do
When I realise with fright
That the spiderman is having me for dinner tonight!

Quietly he laughs and shaking his head
Creeps closer now
Closer to the foot of the bed
And softer than shadow and quicker than flies
His arms are all around me and his tongue in my eyes
"Be still be calm be quiet now my precious boy
Don't struggle like that or I will only love you more
For it's much too late to get away or turn on the light
The spiderman is having you for dinner tonight"

And I feel like I'm being eaten
By a thousand million shivering furry holes
And I know that in the morning I will wake up
In the shivering cold
And the spiderman is always hungry...

FASCINATION STREET

Oh it's opening time
Down on Fascination Street
So let's cut the conversation
And get out for a bit
Because I feel it all fading
And paling
And I'm begging
To drag you down with me
To kick the last nail in
Yeah I like you in that
Like I like you to scream
But if you open your mouth
Then I can't be responsible
For quite what goes in
Or to care what comes out
So just pull on your hair
Just pull on your pout
And let's move to the beat
Like we know that it's over
If you slip going under
Slip over my shoulder
So just pull on your face
Just pull on your feet
And let's hit opening time
Down on Fascination Street

So pull on your hair
Pull on your pout
Cut the conversation
Just open your mouth
Pull on your face
Pull on your feet
And let's hit opening time
Down on Fascination Street

PRAYERS FOR RAIN

You shatter me
Your grip on me
A hold on me
So dull it kills
You stifle me
Infectious sense
Of hopelessness
And prayers for rain
I suffocate
I breathe in dirt
And nowhere shines
But desolate
And drab the hours
All spent
On killing time again
All waiting for
The rain

You fracture me
Your hands on me
A touch so plain
So stale it kills
You strangle me
Entangle me
In hopelessness
And prayers for rain
I deteriorate
I live in dirt
And nowhere glows
But drearily
And tired the hours
All spent
On killing time again
All waiting for the rain

PICTURES OF YOU

I've been looking so long at these pictures of you
That I almost believe that they're real
I've been living so long with my pictures of you
That I almost believe
That the pictures are all I can feel

Remembering
You standing quiet in the rain
As I ran to your heart to be near
And we kissed as the sky fell in
Holding you close
How I always held close in your fear
Remembering
You running soft through the night
You were bigger and brighter and wider than snow
And screamed at the make-believe
Screamed at the sky
And you finally found all your courage
To let it all go

Remembering
You fallen into my arms
Crying for the death of your heart
You were stone white
So delicate
Lost in the cold
You were always so lost in the dark
Remembering
You how you used to be
Slow drowned
You were angels
So much more than everything
Oh hold for the last time then slip away quietly
Open my eyes
But I never see anything

If only I'd thought of the right words
I could have held onto your heart
If only I'd thought of the right words
I wouldn't be breaking apart
All my pictures of you

Looking so long at these pictures of you
But I never hold onto your heart
Looking so long for the words to be true
But always just breaking apart
My pictures of you

There was nothing in the world
That I ever wanted more
Than to feel you deep in my heart
There was nothing in the world
That I ever wanted more
Than to never feel the breaking apart
All my pictures ot you

DISINTEGRATION

Oh I miss the kiss of treachery
The shameless kiss of vanity
The soft and the black and the velvety
Up tight against the side of me
And mouth and eyes and heart all bleed
And run in thickening streams of greed
As bit by bit it starts the need
To just let go
My party piece

Oh I miss the kiss of treachery
The aching kiss before I feed
The stench of a love for a younger meat
And the sound that it makes
When it cuts in deep
The holding up on bended knees
The addiction of duplicities
As bit by bit it starts the need
To just let go
My party piece

But I never said I would stay to the end
So I leave you with babies
And hoping for frequency
Screaming like this in the hope of the secrecy
Screaming me over and over and over
I leave you with photographs
Pictures of trickery
Stains on the carpet
And stains on the scenery
Songs about happiness murmured in dreams
When we both of us knew
How the ending would be...

So it's all come back round to
Breaking apart again
Breaking apart like I'm made up of glass again
Making it up behind my back again
Holding my breath for the fear of sleep again
Holding it up behind my head again
Cut in deep to the heart of the bone again
Round and round and round
And it's coming apart again
Over and over and over

Now that I know that I'm breaking to pieces
I'll pull out my heart
And I'll feed it to anyone
Crying for sympathy
Crocodiles cry for the lover of the crowd
And the three cheers from everyone
Dropping through sky
Through the glass of the roof
Through the roof of your mouth
Through the mouth of your eye
Through the eye of the needle
It's easier for me to get closer to heaven
Than ever feel whole again

I never said I would stay to the end
I knew I would leave you
With babies and everything
Screaming like this
In the hole of sincerity
Screaming me over and over and over
I leave you with photographs
Pictures of trickery
Stains on the carpet
And stains on the memory
Songs about happiness murmured in dreams
When we both of us knew
How the end always is...

How the end always is...

UNTITLED

Hopelessly drift
In the eyes of the ghost again
Down on my knees
And my hands in the air again
Pushing my face
In the memory of you again
But I never know if it's real
Never know how I wanted to feel
Never quite said
What I wanted to say to you
Never quite managed the words
To explain to you
Never quite knew
How to make them believable
And now the time has gone
Another time undone
Hopelessly fighting the devil
Futility
Feeling the monster
Climb deeper inside of me
Feeling him gnawing my heart away
Hungrily
I'll never lose this pain
Never dream of you again

LAST DANCE

I'm so glad you came
I'm so glad you remembered
To see how we're ending
Our last dance together
Expectant
Too punctual
But prettier than ever
I really believe that this time it's forever

But older than me now
More constant
More real
And the fur and the mouth and the innocence
Turned to hair and contentment
That hangs in abasement
A woman now standing
Where once there was only a girl

I'm so glad you came
I'm so glad you remembered
The walking through walls in the heart of December
The blindness of happiness
Of falling down laughing
And I really believed that this time was forever

But Christmas falls late now
Flatter and colder
And never as bright as when we used to fall
All this in an instant
Before I can kiss you
A woman now standing where once
There was only a girl

I'm so glad you came
I'm so glad you remembered
To see how we're ending our last dance together
Reluctantly
Cautiously
But prettier than ever
I really believe that this time it's forever

But Christmas falls late now
Flatter and colder
And never as bright as when we used to fall
And even if we drink
I don't think we would kiss in the way that we did
When the woman
Was only a girl

HOMESICK

Hey hey!
Just one more
And I'll walk away
All the everything you win
Turns to nothing today
And I forget how to move
When my mouth is this dry
And my eyes are bursting hearts
In a blood-stained sky
Oh it was sweet
It was wild
And oh how we...
I trembled stuck in honey
Honey cling to me
So just one more
Just one more go
Inspire in me
The desire in me
To never go home

Oh just one more
And I'll walk away
All the everything you win
Turns to nothing today
So just one more
Just one more go
Inspire in me
The desire in me
To never go home

BABBLE

Nothing ever changes
Nothing ever moves
I swim around in circles
In the same old lifeless room
And talk about the mirror man
The whispers in my ear again
The hot and sticky pillow man
Is smothering my face again

Nothing ever changes
Nothing ever moves
And I run around hysterical
In dead persistent gloom
And babble out in simile
Like dog-head-monkey-music me
Shut up shut up shut up shut up
Shut up!!!
And let me breathe...

OUT OF MIND

I've been up for days
And I feel like a menagerie
I'm scratching 'til I bleed
And I keep on seeing
Imaginary lemurs
In the street
In the middle of the day
But as long as I can breathe
Then I know I'll be OK
I'll be alright
I'm out of mind
I'm out of sight
I'm out of sight

I've been up for days
And I feel like a laboratory rat
Inside a maze
And I reel in the monotony of
Screaming
At the moon
In the middle of the day
But as long as I can see it
Then I know I'll be OK
I'll be fine
I'm out of sight
I'm completely out of mind
Completely out of mind

OK
Alright
Come and watch me shake tonight
Mouth wide
Soft and bright
Bite my hand and scream
OK
Alright
Come and watch me break tonight
Push deep
Out of sight
Bit my hand and hold on tight...

FEAR OF GHOSTS

Like a feeling that I'm down
Down inside my heart
Like I'm looking out through
Splitting bloodred
Windows in my heart
From a higher up than heaven
And a harder down than stone
Shake the fear that always clawing
Pulls me clawing down alone
As I spitting splitting bloodred
Breaking windows in my heart
And the past is taunting
Fear of ghosts
Is forcing me apart
And the further I get
From the things that I care about
The less I care about
How much further away I get...

I am lost again
With everything gone
And more alone
Than I have ever been
I expect you to understand
To feel it too
But I know that even if you will
You cannot ever help me
Nor can I
Ever help you

2 LATE

So I'll wait for you
Where I always wait
Behind the signs that sell the news
I'll watch for you like yesterday
And hope for you
One day that once
Spent out on me
And up 'til late
I search for you
Your hat pushed straight
Away from me
Your measured step
Heads up you win
Always too late

If I could just once catch your eye
Invisible against the words
That hold you down in solitude
And never let you go
The way that every time
My eyes just close
Like lids of wooden men in file
I put you under rainy day
Your hat's all off
And I'm gone away